Learning
Can Be Fun!

by Suzanne Briggs

Book 2

Syllable Division for Word Attack Skills

with activities to support
structured multisensory language programmes

Egon Publishers Ltd

Learning Can Be Fun!
Book 2

Revised Edition 1999
Second Impression 2001
Second Edition 2013

Egon Publishers Ltd
618 Leeds Road, Outwood
Wakefield, West Yorkshire, WF1 2LT
Company Reg'n: 1336483

Copyright (c) Suzanne Briggs, MA, Froebel, AMBDA

Illustrated by Rose
using original ideas of
Nicky Robertson

ISBN: 978 1907656 03 3

Lisa Chisholm

Contents

Introduction

This book of structured syllable games and exercises has been devised to develop pupils' skills in reading, writing and spelling within an integrated programme to improve standards of literacy. It can be used from the reception year to early secondary school levels to reinforce these skills in an enjoyable way during the daily literacy lessons.

The games and worksheets follow a multisensory approach and can be used to support structured language courses such as 'The Hickey Multisensory Language Course'. There are ten targets to be completed covering the four syllable division rules.

The activities provide reinforcement when learning and practice for all pupils, identifying those who have early difficulties in reading and spelling. The activities in 'Phonological Awareness' and 'Alphabet Sequencing' ('Learning Can Be Fun!' Books 0 & 1) can be introduced at the same time.

The author has worked for over 30 years with pupils with dyslexia and was co-editor of 'The Hickey Multisensory Language Course', 2nd Edition, 1992. Her research (Briggs, 1997) examined the 'Management and Transfer of Structured Language Teaching to the Classroom' and has successfully benefitted many children in the classroom. As a tutor and trainer of teachers, she has shown how the classroom teacher can identify and help children with learning difficulties, including those who are bilingual, by using these games. The exercises and games in this series of books have been collected over a number of years from teachers following specialist courses.

This book contains:

   a) A selection of games to develop word attack skills using syllable division rules for reading and spelling.

   b) Worksheets to reinforce the rules taught.

   c) A record sheet, to be photocopied, and coloured in as the pupils complete each target worksheet and can read and spell the words.

Explaining the Syllable Division Rules

Many pupils devise their own rules when tackling words for reading and spelling in order to acquire written language skills. Others have no word attack skills and need to be taught how to divide words into syllables following a step by step multisensory structured routine. A pupil requires a high coding ability to look at a whole word and read it. This is a difficulty for many pupils with dyslexic tendencies.

Pupils who have problems in acquiring written language skills have a difficulty with phonological processing, especially dyslexics. They may have either a poor auditory or visual short-term memory which affects their coding and sequencing ability. Many, therefore, need to work from the part (i.e. the syllable) to the whole word using a multisensory routine for words that can be sounded out, as well as training visualisation skills to read and spell sight words. The basic concepts when teaching syllable division in multisyllabic words need to be grasped first, then the pupils are shown how to use the rules in a flexible way.

Targets 1, 2, 3, 4 – Closed and open syllables

a) First teach the pupils to identify syllables in words with games (toys /pictures).

b) Then introduce the definitions of closed and open syllables and always mark the word from the first vowel.

c) Give practice for the pupils to recognize these syllables. The concepts of the base word patterns (always marked from the first vowel) of the closed syllable (e.g. V.C. words as in 'hop', 'run') and the open syllable (e.g. V. words as in 'go', 'no', or syllables as in 'ho' in ho / tel) need to be recognized easily.

Targets 5, 6, - V̆C / CV words with two closed syllables

Introduce the concept of two closed syllable words for reading when the pupils can recognise base word patterns. Divide the word between the two consonants, e.g.

$$\underline{\text{V̆ C / C V}}$$
kid   nap

Target 6 (ii) – Never divide a diphthong, e.g. 'th', 'sh', etc.

In words where there are more than two consonants between the vowels never divide the diphthong. This usually occurs in compound words where two words have been joined together, e.g.

bath / room   en / thuse   wish / ful

Target 7 – V̄/C V words with first syllable open

In words with one consonant between the two vowels the syllables are usually divided after the first vowel, e.g.

$$\frac{\text{V̄} \ / \ \text{C} \ \text{V}}{\text{ba} \ / \ \text{con}}$$

Teach the pupils to always use the regular rules first, i.e. with the long vowel in the first open syllable. Practice using these rules. Then in Target 8, teach the irregular rule, i.e. the short vowel sound in the first closed syllable.

Target 8 – V̆C / V irregular words with first syllable closed

a) In irregular words with one consonant between two vowels the syllables are divided after the consonant when the first vowel has a short sound, e.g.

$$\frac{\text{V̆} \ \text{C} / \ \text{V}}{\text{hab} \ / \ \text{it}}$$

b) Teach the pupils to work flexibly by applying these rules. They need to be aware of the Irregular Rule of the V̆C / C syllable and to use it when the work does not sound right when following the regular pattern of V̄ / CV, e.g.

Stage 1

$$\frac{\text{V̄} \ / \ \text{C} \ \text{V}}{\text{ro} \ / \ \text{bin}}$$

Stage 2

$$\frac{\text{V̆} \ \text{C} \ / \ \text{V}}{\text{rob} \ / \ \text{in}} \ \sqrt{}$$

Target 9 – Multisyllable words

a) In multisyllable words it is necessary to learn to work flexibly. Mark the pattern from one vowel to the next and divide between the syllables. Continue to the next vowel and mark the word pattern when you have divided the first syllables, e.g.

Stage 1	Stage 2
V̆ C / C V	V̆ C / C V
fan / tastic	fan / tas / tic

b) The worksheets give the pupil the practice and confidence in applying the syllable division rules in a flexible way when working with longer words, e.g.

dem / on / stra / tion   ren / o / va / tion

c) Divide between two vowels that are not working together to make one sound. Do not divide a final syllable, e.g.

di / et   po / et   or   ex / pec / ta / tion

Target 10 – The Individual 'i'

a) The vowel 'i' is an individual letter which can stand on its own in a syllable. It usually gives its short sound (ĭ) even though it appears to be in an open syllable. This is often referred to as the connective 'i' and occurs in a great number of words, e.g.

individual (ĭ)   as it is very   in / dĭ / vĭ / du / al

b) The other vowels usually keep their long sound when ending an open syllable. Practice is needed in reading and spelling multisyllabic words following all syllable division rules in a flexible way. (See Target 10 (ii)).

c) The rules and exercises can be practiced with words using a computer word processing program.

Syllable Division Record Target Sheet

Colour in a target when the words can be read
and spelt on each worksheet.

Pupil's Name: _____   Date: _____

Target 2
Worksheet 1

Target 2
Worksheet 2

Target 3
Worksheet 1

Target 3
Worksheet 2

Target 4
Worksheet 1

Target 6 (i)
Worksheet 1

Target 6 (i)
Worksheet 2

Target 6 (i)
Worksheet 3

Target 6 (i)
Worksheet 4

Target 6 (ii)
Worksheet 1

Target 6 (ii)
Worksheet 2

Target 6 (ii)
Worksheet 3

Target 6 (ii)
Worksheet 4

Target 7
Worksheet 1

Syllable Division Record Target Sheet

Colour in a target when the words can be read
and spelt on each worksheet.

Pupil's Name: _____   Date: _____

Target 7
Worksheet 2

Target 9
Worksheet 2

Target 7
Worksheet 3

Target 10 (i)
Worksheet 1

Target 8
Worksheet 1

Target 10 (i)
Worksheet 2

Target 8
Worksheet 2

Target 10 (ii)
Worksheet 1

Target 8
Worksheet 3

Target 10 (ii)
Worksheet 2

Target 8
Worksheet 4

Target 10 (ii)
Worksheet 3

Target 9
Worksheet 1

Target 10 (ii)
Worksheet 4

Target 1

Identifying Syllables
Understand and learn the definition of a syllable.

Definition: 'A syllable is a beat in a word'

Syllable name games

Use the names of children, animals, vegetables. Beat out the syllables in each word.

Different movements or musical instruments can be used:

a) Clap hands

b) Stamp feet

c) Tap the table

d) Beat drums or other musical instruments

e) Count beats with fingers

f)   Tap beats on legs or arms

g) Draw chalk boxes on the floor and ask pupils to hop or jump into each box as they segment words

a SYLLABLE is a beat in a word

Target 1

Identifying Syllables
Using awareness of the senses to aid memory skills.

1. Developing the use of descriptive, expressive language, in naming and identifying objects.

2. Syllable segmentation.

Basket games

Materials needed:

a) Small basket for toys and objects that can be named with more than one syllable, e.g. teddy bear, clothes peg, ambulance, toothbrush, screwdriver.

b) A board game with squares, e.g. Ludo, race track, etc.

Ideas:

1. **Name Game**. Discuss the names of objects. Ask students to think of another name for...? Each pupil in turn selects an object from the basket, names it and beats out the syllables. Decide how the syllables will be beaten out or counted using actions and movement. This is an excellent way of developing the use of vocabulary and language.

2. **Board game**. Ideal for playing in small groups. Each player has a piece or counter they move on 1 space for each syllable in a word that they say when naming an object taken from the basket.

3. **Extra syllables**. A longer name or description of a chosen object can score more points, e.g. 'screw / driv / er' = 3 points; but 'a screwdriver is a tool' = 8 points. This encourages the use of expressive language.

4. **Use of numbers**. Counting bricks can be used to see how many points the pupils score for each syllable in their words. The scores may be doubled, or add five points each time, to bring in computational skills and ensure success if a board game is being played.

5. **Hidden objects (sensory games)**. Objects are taken from the basket and put into a cloth bag. A pupil is chosen to feel an object and describe it to the class, giving the number of syllables in the word; or the pupils ask questions about the object to try to guess the name. This is a valuable game to develop expressive language skills. Alternatively, objects with a smell can be placed in jars, the children close their eyes and try to identify the smell or describe it, e.g. onion, garlic, etc.

6. **Kim's game (visual memory game)**. Objects are taken from the basket and put on a tray. First use objects with one syllable words, then two, then three.The pupils study the objects and the tray is then covered with a cloth and the pupils are asked to recall the names of the objects on the tray. Ask what stategies they used to remember the objects.

7. **Kim's game (grouping or classifying objects)**. Objects are taken from the basket and arranged into groups, e.g. animals, colours, sizes, etc. Do not tell the children that the objects can be remembered in sets but ask them what memory strategies they might use to memorise the objects on the tray. Discuss why some objects belong together. Ask them why some objects are the same or different. Use a variety of items that can be identified by touch, smell, sound or taste. Pupils will then develop an awareness of using their senses. Put sets of objects in the basket and ask the students to sort them into groups.

8. **Auditory game**. Read the children a list of objects to be remembered. In the beginning use lists that are ordered and have links, e.g. fruit, animals. Ask them how they memorised the list.

9. **Memory pictures**. Read the children a list of objects to be remembered. Suggest they listen with their eyes closed and try to visualise the objects as the list is read. Ask them to tell others what they can see.

10. **Class project**. Put objects into the basket to introduce a class project, e.g. a number of different animals. Ask where do the animals live? In what type of 'home', climate, etc. Try to find out what pupils already know rather than teaching a list such as, stable, sty, etc. Discuss how they plan to find out more information.

Target 1

Identifying Syllables
Use of visual and auditory senses

1. Identify and name objects in pictures using receptive and expressive language.

2. Reinforce syllables counted in words.

Materials needed:

a) A games board, e.g. car or horse race track, ludo, snakes and ladders, etc.

b) A set of syllable picture cards with 2, 3, 4, and 5 syllable words and pictures.

c) A set of cards numbered 1 - 6.

To play:

1. **Board Game**. Place the syllable cards face down on the table. First player takes a card and names the object in the picture and counts out the syllables. Pupil then moves his counter on 2, 3, or 4 places according to how many syllables are in the word.

2. **Use of numbers**. As above with the number of points being doubled for each word.

3. **Pairs memory game**. Spread the syllable picture word cards out face down on the table. Each player turns over two cards at a time in order to find a matching pair. The aim is to find two cards with the same number of syllables in order to win a pair.

4. **Three of a kind**. Place the numbered cards face up on the table. Then place the syllable cards face down. First player takes a picture card names it and places it with the correct syllable number to form a column. The player who places the third card in a column names all three pictures to win the set.

Target 2

Closed Syllables

Warning: Do not move on to using letters in words until the pupils are ready and can identify syllables as they name objects and pictures.

Definition:
1. A syllable is closed when there is one or more consonants after the vowel. It closes in the short vowel sound.

2. Every syllable must have a vowel sound. As this stage vowels can be coloured red and referred to as 'red letters'.

Syllable house

Make a syllable house to introduce the concepts of open and closed syllables, which are the first key stages to decoding multisyllable words.

Materials needed for each pupil:
Blank rectangular sheet of paper, A4 or A5
Red and black crayons (or pens), scissors

Instructions:
1. Turn the paper to 'portrait' position and fold bottom to the top and press down along the fold.
2. Repeat this to make 4 equal rows, then open the sheet of paper out
3. Turn paper to 'landscape' position and take the bottom up to the top and fold and press.
You now have a sheet of paper divided into 8 squares.
4. In squares 2 and 3 draw windows, in square 7 draw a door with a door knob on the right, then cut along right hand edge and the top of the door.
5. In squares 5, 6 and 7 write the letters 'g' , 'o' (in red) and 't'.
6. Open the door and fold it to the left then write the letter 'o' in red on the back of the door.
7. Demonstrate closed and open syllables by reading the words as the door is closed (got) and open (go).

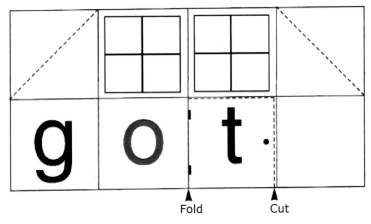

21

Target 2

Closed Syllables

Definition:
1. A syllable is closed when there is one or more consonants after the vowel. It closes in the short vowel sound.

2. Every syllable must have a vowel sound. As this stage vowels can be coloured red and referred to as 'red letters'. The word pattern is V̆C or V̆CC.

  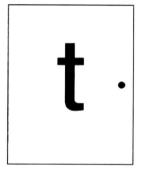

Game

Materials:

1. Five counters for each pupil.

2. Make a set of one syllable cards with closed and open syllables. E.g. cat, dog, hop, hat, fun, run, pig, skip, sit, no, cra, ste, tra, me, ba, to, bu, si, cu.

Worksheets: (see following pages)

To play:

1. Teacher holds up a card.
2. Show the pictures or letters (visual).
3. Read the word or syllable aloud (auditory).
4. Pupils hold up a counter when they think they have identified a closed syllable word.
5. Winner is the pupil who correctly identifies 5 closed syllables.

A CLOSED SYLLABLE HAS AT LEAST ONE CONSONANT
AFTER THE VOWEL AND THE SOUND IS SHORT

Target 2

Closed Syllables

Worksheet 1

1. Mark the vowels in red.
2. Draw a square or door round the consonant(s) that follow the vowel in the closed syllable.
3. All words have a pattern. Mark the pattern from the first vowel of each closed syllable word putting 'V' over the vowel and 'C' over the following consonants.

h e	s o	n o d
h e n	s o b	n o
w e	i n	b i
w e t	l	b i t
t h e n	m i	s a t
r e	m i l k	s a
g o	s h e d	m e
g o t	s h e	m e l t

Target 2

Closed Syllables

Worksheet 2

1. Mark the vowels in red.
2. Draw a square or door round the consonant(s) that follow the vowel in the closed syllable.
3. All words have a pattern. Mark the pattern from the first vowel of each closed syllable word putting 'V' over the vowel and 'C' over the following consonants.

n a	s e t	t r i
p i t	p r o	b a d
p u	p i n k	m o
d e	p l o d	p a
s t u n	b e n d	c a
s t e	t o p	b r o
t u	r o t	m o
p i c k	b e	h a t
s p i	t e n t	d u
b a	f a n	s t o

Target 3

Open Syllables

Definition:
1. A syllable is open when there is no consonant after the vowel.
   The vowel ends the open syllable and gives its long sound.

2. The word pattern is pattern is 'V'.

Game

Materials:

1. Five counters for each pupil.
2. Set of one syllable cards with closed and open syllables.
3. 2 cards marked 'Open syllables' and 'Closed syllables'.

Worksheets: (see following pages)

To play:

1. Play the same game as in Target 2, but now the aim is to identify
   the syllables.
2. Syllable sort. Sort the syllable cards and place them under the
   cards marked 'closed syllables' and 'open syllables'.

**AN OPEN SYLLABLE HAS NOTHING
AFTER THE VOWEL AND THE SOUND IS LONG**

Target 3

Open Syllables

Worksheet 1

1. Mark the vowels in red.
2. All the words have a pattern. Mark the word pattern from the first vowel of the open syllables putting 'V' over the vowel.
3. Put these open syllables into longer words, e.g. 'ta' as in table.

t a	s i p	p i
h e n	w o	s p i n
p u	b o d	b e
s p a	r o	f u
j u m p	m e	b r o
w i n k	d i n	j o
p i n	s t e	h o p
f l i p	h i n t	b u
p l a	s i	s t o p
f e l t	d e	j i n x

Target 3

Open Syllables

Martian words

1. Can you find the open syllables?
2. How quickly can you read these 'Martian' words?

d o m b	s n a d	s l e
s p i n t	c r o d	b l i n t
t h a	m o	p u n c
t r a x	s l o x	p l e n
d r e n t	s h i l d	t r u
q u i l	h u s t	s w u
g u	b o n	p l i
f l u g	t w a	g l o g

Target 4

Short Vowel Sounds

1. Short vowel discrimination.
2. Identify the missing vowels.
3. First steps to reading for comprehension and writing a story.

Sammy's Fishing Story
1. Copy of Sammy's Fishing Story (see opposite).
2. Red pencils.
3. Short vowel reference work card.

Work card:
1. Make a key card for the short vowel sounds.

(ă)   (ĕ)   (ĭ)   (ŏ)   (ŭ)

   Explain that the brackets denote the sound of a letter.
   A breve ˘ is the sign used for short vowel sounds.
2. Pupils draw their own picture clue beneath each letter.
3. Pupils fill in the blanks to complete 'Sammy's Fishing Story'.

Worksheet:
1. Each pupil fills in the missing vowels in 'Sammy's Fishing Story' using the red pencil or pen.
2. The story has been left blank at the end for pupils to complete in their own way and/or to draw a picture.

To play:
1. Pupil make up their own stories leaving out the short vowels for another pupil to complete.
2. Suggested titles:

The Spider	The Old Shed	The Robbery
The Red Ship	The Bad Dog	The Funny Boy

Target 4

Sammy's Fishing Story

Worksheet 1   (ǎ)   (ě)   (ǐ)   (ǒ)   (ǔ)

S _ mm _   h _ s   a   b _ g   f _ t   f _ sh

_ n   h _ s   r _ d.   He   p _ t   _ t

_ nto   h _ s   n _ t.   Th _   bl _ ck   c _ t

j _ mps   _ nt _   th _   n _ t   t _   g _ t

th _   f _ sh.   Sh _   _ s   h _ ngr _ .

S _ mm _   y _ lls   _ s   h _   fl _ ngs

h _ s   c _ p   _ t   th _   b _ d   c _ t.

Th _   c _ t   gr _ bs   th _   f _ sh   _ nd

r _ ns.   S _ mm _   tw _ sts   h _ s   l _ g

_ s   h _   f _ lls   _ nd ....

29

Target 5

Closed syllable words
Find the missing vowels in multisyllable words
V̆C /CV words

1. Short vowel discrimination in words with two syllables.
2. Identify the word pattern and say 'vowel-consonant-consonant-vowel'.
3. Explain use of abbreviations, e.g. VCCV.

Bingo

Materials:

1. Prepared cards (see following pages).
2. Plastic covers for the cards.
3. Red pencil for each pupil.

To play: (auditory, visual, kinaesthetic)

1. Teacher reads out a word.
2. Pupils listen and search for the word on their card.
3. Pupils identify their word saying the missing vowel sounds aloud.
4. Pupils write the missing vowels in red in their word,
   e.g. b _ nd _ t , insert 'a' and 'i' to read 'bandit'.
5. The first pupil to complete the words on their card is the winner.

Teaching points:

1. Point out patterns in the words.
2. A word pattern is always marked from the first vowel to the next vowel.
3. Ask them to write words from the Bingo cards.
4. Every syllable has at least one vowel. Make the vowels red so that they can see how many syllables there are in a word.
5. Draw a line above the word.
5. Mark the word patterns from the first vowel to the next vowel. (The pattern of these words is 'VCCV').

Syllable division:

Students can type out words using a word processing programme.
They can practice dividing the words into syllables using '/' following the pattern V̆C / CV.

Closed Syllable Words - Bingo Card 1

b _ nd _ t	p _ pp _ t	w _ mb _ t
h _ sb _ nd	_ ps _ t	g _ ss _ p
g _ bl _ t	m _ mm _ l	f _ ss _ l
m _ gg _ t	m _ sc _ t	t _ mp _ r

Closed Syllable Words - Bingo Card 2

r _ sc _ l	p _ st _ l	s _ dd _ n
c _ ct _ s	c _ tl _ t	p _ tr _ l
t _ lc _ m	j _ mp _ ng	s _ gn _ l
c _ mb _ t	r _ mp _ s	t _ nd _ m

Closed Syllable Words - Bingo Card 3

w _ gw _ m	s _ lk _ ng	ch _ ck _ n
v _ lv _ t	g _ bl _ n	cr _ ck _ r
h _ lm _ t	k _ dn _ p	m _ gn _ t
p _ cn _ c	d _ nt _ st	t _ bl _ t

Closed Syllable Words - Bingo Card 4

r _ bb _ t	t _ nn _ s	tr _ mp _ t
pl _ st _ c	B _ tm _ n	s _ sp _ ct
cr _ ck _ t	sp _ ll _ ng	h _ mb _ g
k _ ck _ ng	gr _ ml _ n	w _ ck _ t

Target 6 (i)

Closed and Open Syllables

CLOSED - V̆C / CV words		OPEN - V̄ / CV words	
ig	loo	sto	len
sup	per	hu	man
kid	nap	cra	zy
ban	dit	ti	dy
bat	man	la	zy
hap	py	fi	nal
rab	bit	ba	con
pup	pet	e	ven

Pairs game 1

1. Give each player 4 to 6 cards with V̆CCV words.
2. Explain Syllable Division Rule 1 (see worksheet 1).
3. Ask players to cut the words on the cards between the two consonants.
4. As they cut each word write 1 on the back of the first syllable card and 2 on the back of the second card.

Pairs game 2

1. Play game as above with V̄ / CV words.
2. Ask players to cut the words after the first vowel.

Pairs game 3

1. Combine words from V̆C / CV and V̄ / CV lists.

To play:

1. When all cards have been cut and numbered deal out the '1' cards.
2. Put the '2' cards face down in a pile.
3. Players place their '1' cards face up on the table and read the syllables aloud.
4. First player takes a card from the '2' pile, reads it aloud, then tries to match to a '1' card to make a complete word. If successful they keep the pairing, if unsuccessful the '2' card is discarded.
5. The next player choses either the discarded card or the next card from the '2' pile.

Worksheets:

1. Complete the worksheets to reinforce the syllable division rules.
2. Speed read the words on each sheet, try to complete the page in less than 20 secs.
3. Use the words as a spelling list, spelling out in syllables.

Target 6 (i)

Syllable Division Rule 1 - V̆C / CV words

Worksheet 1

1. Mark the vowels in red.
2. Mark the word pattern from the first vowel: VCCV.
3. Divide the syllables between the two consonants.
4. Read the syllables aloud.
5. Try spelling the words.

_____ kidnap	_____ magnet	_____ batman
_____ intend	_____ disgust	_____ connect
_____ picnic	_____ sandal	_____ rascal
_____ twisted	_____ zigzag	_____ talcum
_____ sapling	_____ velvet	_____ public

Target 6 (i)

Syllable Division Rule 1 - V̆C / CV words

Worksheet 2

1. Mark the vowels in red.
2. Mark the word pattern from the first vowel: VCCV.
3. Divide the syllables between the two consonants.
4. Read the syllables aloud.
5. Try spelling the words.

_____	_____	_____
pistol	canvas	splendid
_____	_____	_____
distant	random	tendon
_____	_____	_____
tennis	collect	infect
_____	_____	_____
gremlin	discuss	impact
_____	_____	_____
extend	pennant	suspect

Target 6 (i)

Syllable Division Rule 1 - V̆C / CV words

Worksheet 3

1. Mark the vowels in red.
2. Mark the word pattern from the first vowel: VCCV.
3. Divide the syllables between the two consonants.
4. Read the syllables aloud.
5. Try spelling the words.

content   insist   dentist

bandit   distant   attend

intact   consist   absent

tonsil   disgust   trumpet

problem   signal   seldom

Target 6 (i)

Syllable Division Rule 1 - V̆C / CV words

Worksheet 4

1. Mark the vowels in red.
2. Mark the word pattern from the first vowel: VCCV.
3. Divide the syllables between the two consonants.
4. Read the syllables aloud.
5. Try spelling the words.

_____	_____	_____
dizzy	dusty	jelly

_____	_____	_____
goblin	soggy	helmet

_____	_____	_____
funny	atlas	silly

_____	_____	_____
album	sudden	frantic

_____	_____	_____
happy	fungus	dentist

Target 6 (ii)

Syllable Division Rule 2 - V̆CCCV words

Worksheet 1

1. Mark the vowels in red.
2. Mark the word pattern from the first vowel.
3. Decide where to divide the syllables between the consonants.
4. Do not divide between dipthongs, e.g. 'th', 'ch', 'sh'.
5. Read the syllables aloud.
6. Try spelling the words.

impress	Alfred	transmit
instant	pilgrim	mistress
bashful	panther	handful
exchange	hamster	snapshot
sunshade	prickly	pilchard
perspex	nostril	address

Target 6 (ii)

Syllable Division Rule 2 - V̆CCCV words

Worksheet 2

1. Mark the vowels in red.
2. Mark the word pattern from the first vowel.
3. Decide where to divide the syllables between the consonants.
4. Do not divide between dipthongs, e.g. 'th', 'ch', 'sh'.
5. Read the syllables aloud.
6. Try spelling the words.

complete	hundred	extreme
instinct	contract	distrust
sandwich	umbrella	monster
subscribe	pamphlet	instruct
inscribe	extract	pumpkin
simply	alphabet	subtract

Target 6 (ii)

Syllable Division Rule 2 - V̆CCCV words

Worksheet 3

1. Mark the vowels in red.
2. Mark the word pattern from the first vowel.
3. Decide where to divide the syllables between the consonants.
4. Do not divide between dipthongs, e.g. 'th', 'ch', 'sh'.
5. Read the syllables aloud.
6. Try spelling the words.

_____	_____	_____
transfer	mongrel	mattress
inspect	bathroom	imprint
express	mushroom	pigsty
helmsman	distress	inspect
transport	handstand	farmyard
ballpoint	ringlet	washroom

Target 6 (ii)

Syllable Division Rule 2 - V̆CCCV words

Worksheet 4

1. Mark the vowels in red.
2. Mark the word pattern from the first vowel: VCCV.
3. Decide where to divide the syllables between the consonants.
4. Do not divide between dipthongs, e.g. 'th', 'ch', 'sh'.
5. Read the syllables aloud.
6. Try spelling the words.

anthem	trombone	ignore
expire	concave	tadpole
include	stampede	cascade
athlete	compose	umpire
sample	explore	advise
purchase	escape	collide

Target 7

Open Syllable Words
Syllable Division Rule 2 - Regular $\bar{V}$ / CV.

Definition:
In words with one consonant between two vowels, the syllables are usually divided after the first vowel.

Bingo   (Missing vowel sounds $\bar{V}$ / CV)

Materials:
1. Prepared cards (see following pages).
2. Plastic covers for the cards.
3. Red pencil for each pupil.

Instructions: (See instructions for the game in Target 5, p.26).

Teaching point:
Remind pupils that 'y' works as a vowel.
e.g. b _ b _ = 'baby' not 'babe'!

Syllable pairs

Materials:
1. Cards printed with open syllable words.
2. Scissors.
3. Worksheets (see following pages).

To play:
1. Prepare cards usng the open syllable word list in Target 6(i), p.29.
2. Follow instructions on p.29 to make game.
3. Play the game following rules for Game 2 on p.29.
4. Play the game using both sets of cards.

Exercises:
1. Complete the following worksheets to reinforce the $\bar{V}$ / CV rule.
2. Transfer this skill to reading by asking pupils to search for words. with a similar pattern in books or newspapers.
3. Tracking exercises can be helpful.
4. Practice the words as a spelling list.

Open Syllable Words - Bingo Card 1

b _ b _	n _ v _	r _ v _ n
l _ d _	st _ d _ nt	d _ t _
_ p _ n	s _ l _ nt	p _ p _ l
c _ p _ d	b _ s _ n	_ d _ l

Open Syllable Words - Bingo Card 2

l _ z _	cr _ c _ s	r _ b _ t
b _ c _ n	f _ n _ l	sp _ d _ r
l _ c _ l	cr _ s _ s	b _ s _ n
r _ c _ nt	p _ l _ t	cr _ z _

Open Syllable Words - Bingo Card 3

h _ z _	p _ p _ r	h _ m _ n
sl _ g _ n	_ qu _ l	pr _ v _ nt
f _ v _ r	t _ t _ m	V _ n _ s
s _ n _ r	_ r _ s	b _ g _ n

Open Syllable Words - Bingo Card 4

l _ l _ c	t _ t _ l	m _ s _ c
h _ t _ l	l _ c _ st	d _ m _ n
h _ m _ d	r _ v _ l	J _ d _
b _ s _ c	h _ r _	V _ k _ ng

Target 7

Syllable Division Rule 2 - $\bar{V}$ / CV words

Worksheet 1

In words with one consonant between two vowels, usually the second syllable begins after the first vowel. Mark the vowel in the first open syllable with a macron ⁻ as the vowel ends the first syllable and the sound is long. This is the regular rule.

1. Mark the vowels in red.
2. Mark the word pattern from the first vowel to the next: $\bar{V}$ / CV.

open	moment	bacon
tiger	baby	silent
nylon	vacant	smiling
crocus	basin	student
lady	unit	tulip
music	judo	emu

Target 7

Syllable Division Rule 2 - V̄ / CV words

Worksheet 2

In words with one consonant between two vowels, usually the second syllable begins after the first vowel. Mark the vowel in the first open syllable with a macron ¯ as the vowel ends the first syllable and the sound is long. This is the regular rule.

   1. Mark the vowels in red.
   2. Mark the word pattern from the first vowel to the next: V̄ / CV.

   _____   _____   _____

super   Roman   idol

total   trident   iris

crazy   resist   detest

depict   gravy   pilot

pretend   coping   result

predict   legal   even

Target 7

Syllable Division Rule 2 - $\bar{V}$ / CV words

Worksheet 3

In words with one consonant between two vowels, usually the second syllable begins after the first vowel. Mark the vowel in the first open syllable with a macron ¯ as the vowel ends the first syllable and the sound is long. This is the regular rule.

1. Mark the vowels in red.
2. Mark the word pattern from the first vowel to the next: $\bar{V}$ / CV.

depend	hotel	request
final	bison	stupid
humid	tidy	local
label	focus	lilac
tuna	demon	lazy
equal	spider	pupil

Target 8

Irregular Syllable Words
Syllable Division Rule 3 - Irregular V̆C / V

Teach the pupils to work flexibly and use the irregular rule if the regular V̄ / CV rule does not work.

Definition:

In irregular words the first syllable is closed, but where there is only one consonant between the two vowels, the syllables are divided after the first consonant, e.g. hăb / it.

Teaching points:

1. Reinforce syllable rules on p2.
2. Teach the irregular V̆C / V rule using following worksheets.
3. Start a search and make a collection of words with the irregular V̆C / V pattern (See list on following page).

Odds and Evens

Materials:

1. Print words from worksheet onto cards.
2. Games board.
3. Dice.
4. Pencil and paper.

To play:

1. Shuffle the cards and play 'Odds and Evens' on a game board.
2. For an even number thrown with the dice the pupil reads two words, for an odd number the pupil reads one word.
3. Use a mix of regular and irregular words. Pupils move their counters on the board, one space for each syllable. Pupils must remember to try the words both ways, first with a long vowel sound and then with a short vowel sound.
4. Use list as a spelling game where the words are read out loud and then written down.

Target 8

Bad 'habit' words
VC / V.

comic	habit	comet	satin
critic	profit	planet	denim
topic	epic	rapid	linen
panic	limit	salad	credit
mimic	visit	solid	camel
relic	tepid	model	static
level	revel	tunic	sever
seven	Devon	valid	profit
canal	pedal	timid	pivot
river	liver	punish	finish
study	copy	gravel	body
city	lily	many	any
pity	Latin	robin	atom
baton	lemon	second	never

Target 8

Syllable Division Rule 3

V̄ / CV or V̆C /V words

Worksheet 1

1. Mark the pattern from the first vowel, V for vowels and C for consonants.
2. Divide the word first with an open syllable and then with a closed syllable, e.g. so / lid or sol / id.
3. Mark the vowel sounds. Syllables could be open ¯, or closed ˘ .
4. Read the words out loud and mark the correct one.

solid	focus	bonus
solid	focus	bonus
tonic	crisis	human
tonic	crisis	human
rapid	demon	limit
rapid	demon	limit
devil	pilot	raven
devil	pilot	raven

Target 8

Syllable Division Rule 3
V̄ / CV or V̆C /V words

Worksheet 2

1. Mark the pattern from the first vowel, V for vowels and C for consonants.
2. Divide the word into syllables, use a ruler or a finger to find the open or closed syllable.
3. Read the word out loud both ways and decide which way to divide it.
4. Add a / to divide the word into the two syllables and mark the first vowel with either a macron ⁻ or a breve ˘ .

dragon	navy	habit
crazy	robin	lazy
solid	locust	comic
denim	apex	pilot
atom	panel	vocal
mimic	gamin	divan
tepid	tulip	final

Target 8

Syllable Division Rules 1, 2 and 3
V̆C / CV   V̄ / CV or V̆C /V words

Worksheet 3

In words with one consonant between two vowels, usually divide syllables after the first vowel. The vowel ends the open syllable and has a long sound.

1. Mark the vowels in red.
2. Mark the pattern from the first vowel.
3. Use the three rules that you have learnt to divide the words into two syllables, V̆C / CV, V̄ / CV and V̆C / V.
4. Read the words.
5. Teach the silent 'e' rule.

decide	trombone	ignore
butane	desire	hostile
visit	erase	insane
dispose	exclude	cabin
invite	level	injure
confuse	arrive	immune

Target 8

Syllable Division Rules 1, 2 & 3

Speed Reading exercise - Use a timer to read these words.

chisel	promote	unit	module
frugal	edit	tropics	lever
biceps	deduct	lunar	medal
submit	moment	respect	suburb
process	fever	chemist	thunder
elope	civil	heron	rotate
propel	helmet	vacate	planet
music	device	tenor	instant
never	moral	spiral	absent
petal	proverb	crater	florist
grocer	temper	digit	superb
metric	scholar	tunic	blazer
escape	divide	perish	madam
punish	rodent	vomit	tulip
evil	sonar	expand	moral
British	lever	proverb	olive

Target 9

Multisyllable Words

Worksheet 1

1. Put a red dot under each vowel.
2. Mark the word pattern from the first vowel to second vowel.
3. Divide the syllables after the first closed syllable, between the two consonants, then continue marking the word pattern.
4. Use all three rules to divide the words.
5. Type the words out on screen and separate the syllables.
6. Study the syllables carefully and use SOS or Visualisation spelling routines to memorise the words.
7. Write each word down spelling the words out loud.
8. Check your spelling, write the words again with your eyes closed.

_____	_____	_____
fantastic	appendix	contraption
_____	_____	_____
Atlantic	yesterday	indignant
_____	_____	_____
defensive	September	attention
_____	_____	_____
allotment	assessment	disposal
_____	_____	_____
extension	nostalgic	interrupt

Target 9

Multisyllable Words

Worksheet 2

1. Put a red dot under each vowel.
2. Mark the word pattern from the first vowel to second vowel.
3. Divide the syllables after the first closed syllable, between the two consonants, then continue marking the word pattern
4. Use all three rules to divide the words.
5. Type the words out on screen and separate the syllables.
6. Study the syllables carefully and use SOS or Visualisation spelling routines to memorise the words.
7. Write each word down spelling the words out loud.
8. Check your spelling, write the words again with your eyes closed.

_____	_____	_____
dislocate	prescription	circulate
_____	_____	_____
bombardment	disappear	admiral
_____	_____	_____
absorbent	buccaneer	collection
_____	_____	_____
commonwealth	deduction	adventure
_____	_____	_____
compartment	impressive	confusion

Target 10 (i)

Syllable Division Rule 4
Individual (ĭ)

Definition:
The vowel 'i' can stand at the end of a syllable and gives its short sound, (ĭ) when it is either an unaccented vowel or used as a connective vowel,
e.g. associate = as / so / cĭ / ate; individual = in / dĭ / vĭ / du / al

Teaching points:
Teach this rule giving the pupils practice with the worksheets on the following pages, then play these games.

Newspaper search

Materials:

1. Cards printed with the words collected.
2. Games board.
3. Newspapers.
4. Computer if possible.

To play:

1. Encourage the pupils to collect five multisyllable words showing Syllable Division Rule 4 that they can find in a newspaper.
2. Write the words down, or type them on screen.
3. Use syllable division rules to divide up the words and read them.

Multisyllable read

Materials:

1. Cards printed with multisyllable words.
2. Games board or a computer.

To play:

1. Each player moves their piece around the board for the number of syllables correctly read.
2. The score can be doubled if the word has been read correctly.
3. Write the words down, or type them on screen.
4. Use syllable division rules to divide up the words and spell them.

Target 10 (i)

Syllable Division Rule 4
Individual (ĭ)

Worksheet 1

1. The vowel 'i' can stand at the end of a syllable and gives its short sound, (ĭ) when it is either an unaccented vowel or used as a connective vowel.
2. Use your knowledge of the syllable division rules but remember that you usually divide a syllable after a vowel, 'i' and it will give the short sound (ĭ),
   e.g. associate = as / so / cĭ / ate; individual = in / dĭ / vĭ / du / al

partition	repetition	actĭvity
condition	attitude	medĭtate
responsible	duplicate	primĭtive
minimum	addition	nominate
division	fumigate	indicate
experiment	solitude	obvious

Target 10 (i)

Syllable Division Rule 4
Individual ĭ

Worksheet 2

1. The vowel 'i' can stand at the end of a syllable and gives its short sound, 'i' , when it is either an unaccented vowel or used as a connective vowel.
2. Use your knowledge of the syllable division rules but remember that you usually divide a syllable after a vowel, 'i' and it will give the short sound (ĭ),
   e.g. associate = as / so / cĭ / ate; individual = in / dĭ / vĭ / du / al

_____	_____	_____
mediate	politics	decision
_____	_____	_____
navigate	aptitude	refrigerate
_____	_____	_____
communicate	position	president
_____	_____	_____
lenient	combination	Africa
_____	_____	_____
motivate	radiant	ridiculous
_____	_____	_____
manipulate	brilliant	expedition

Target 10 (ii)

Multisyllable Hop

Worksheet 1

1. Use all of the syllable division rules to see how quickly you can read and divide these words.
2. Use a timer to check how quick you are.

_____
wigwam

_____
impress

_____
motive

_____
equal

_____
tonic

_____
fantastic

_____
pantomime

_____
individual

_____
contribution

_____
experimentation

Target 10 (ii)

Multisyllable Division

Worksheet 2

1. Use your knowledge of the syllable division rules to divide these words.
2. Type the words on screen and separate the syllables.
3. Study the syllables. Use SOS or Visualisation spelling techniques.
4. Write the words down and check your spelling.

brilliant	candidate	clarinet
classical	astronaut	boisterous
navigate	expected	asparagus
attention	compliment	artichoke
diplomat	dinosaur	persecute

Target 10 (ii)

Multisyllable Division

Worksheet 3

1. Use your knowledge of the syllable division rules to divide these words.
2. Type the words on screen and separate the syllables.
3. Study the syllables. Use SOS or Visualisation spelling techniques.
4. Write the words down and check your spelling.

_____	_____	_____
caterpillar	apparatus	apparition
binocular	callisthenics	commiserate
congregation	superintend	reproduction
reservation	apprehension	aggravating
disinfectant	employment	expansion

Target 10 (ii)

Multisyllable Division

Worksheet 4

1. Use your knowledge of the syllable division rules to divide these words.
2. Type the words on screen and separate the syllables.
3. Study the syllables. Use SOS or Visualisation spelling techniques.
4. Write the words down and check your spelling.

_____	_____	_____
expectation	explosion	contraction
_____	_____	_____
approximately	immigration	requirement
_____	_____	_____
successively	recollection	appropriate
_____	_____	_____
occasionally	exagerate	parliament
_____	_____	_____
constitution	credential	opportunity

Appendix

Multisensory Spelling Techniques

Stage 1 - Study the words

1. Can you read the words to be learnt?
2. Check the meanings of the words.
3. Put them into a sentence.
4. Do any of the words have a similar spelling pattern?
5. Can you find small words in the large words, believe = be - lie.
6. Learn the easier words first.

Stage 2 - SOS (Simultaneous Oral Spelling) spelling technique

1. Say the word aloud as you look at it.
2. Break or cut the word into syllables.
3. Spell the letters out aloud.
4. Trace the word, cover the word.
5. Spell by naming the letters aloud as you write the word from memory.
6. Check the spelling.
7. With eyes closed, write the word again, spell the letters aloud as you write.
8. Check the spelling and if correct, move on to the next word.

Stage 3 - Use √NLP (Neuro-Linguistic Programming) visualisation skills to train the memory

1. Relax, think of something you enjoy or which makes you laugh.
2. Colour in the difficult parts or syllables of the word.
3. Study the word, move the eyes up and picture it on a blank wall.
4. Name the letters aloud as you imagine them being laser beamed in syllables onto the wall.
5. Without taking the eyes away, give the letters in reverse order.
6. Imagine the difficult letters in a bigger size, or colour.
7. Write the word down, eyes open, spelling the letters aloud, and then check spelling.
8. Write the woprd with eyes closed, spellling the letters aloud and then in a dictation sentence.